TO MOM

by children
for mothers everywhere
edited by
Richard and Helen Exley

Houghton Mifflin Company
Boston

To Dad (a companion to this volume)

First American publication, 1978

Library of Congress Cataloging in Publication Data
Main entry under title:

To mom, by children for mothers everywhere.

A revision of the ed. published by Exley
Publications, Watford, Herts., Eng. under title:
To mum.

SUMMARY: Children describe their mothers and
characterize the mother-child relationship.

1. Mothers — Addresses, essays, lectures.
2. Mother and child — Addresses, essays, lectures.
3. Children's writings. [1. Mothers — Addresses,
essays, lectures. 2. Children's writings]
I. Exley, Richard.   II. Exley, Helen.
III. Freedman, Miriam K.
HQ759.T63 1978   301.42′12   78-2874
ISBN 0-395-26733-1

Printed in the United States of America

N 10 9 8 7 6 5 4 3 2

Warm thanks to Miriam K. Freedman for her
editorial assistance.

To: _____

_____

_____

From: _____

_____

_____

Faith Gibbon

What is a mom?

Moms are walls which protect their children from the outside world.
Adrian Leto Age 11

Moms are the people who tell you that you need a coat on in a heatwave and that you're still too young to have the radio-control airplane that you've wanted since you were three.
William

A mother is a female parent. Someone to wake you too early and make you go to bed too early, and someone to see that you *always* practice your piano.
Susan Age 11

Mothers are for tucking kids in bed.
Pam Munroe Age 11

A mom is a woman who buys you candy and when you have fillings at the dentist she blames you.
Aishling

Moms are for letting you get out of washing the dishes because your favorite program is on television.
Ruby Oliveua Age 13

A mom is someone who when you want to watch a football game she wants to watch a love story.
Bret Monis Age 11

A mom is a person that is always in the right place when you need her.
Claire Bagguely

Moms put Band-Aids on your knee when you fall over and come to see your football game when they don't really want to.
David Champneys Age 10

A mom is supposed to love you and wash boys' smelly socks.

Sally Arthy

Birgitte Nielsen Age 11

A mommy puts up with a lot of things like work and children.
Jennifer McGloin Age 9

A mother is someone some people take for granted.
Paula White Age 13

A mom is a woman who says "go to bed" and when she says that, you stay very quite and she forgets about you.
Aishling Nolan

A mom is a person who looks after you if you get scared, and if you want your teddy bear. *Elizabeth Bird Age 8*

Moms drive you ten times around town on Sunday, looking for funny chimneys to report to the teacher.
Timothy Robinson Age 12

A mom is a person who lets you creep in beside her to watch the horror movie (when Dad is out).
Suzanne Pinder Age 12

Moms are people who are angry when you're at home and sad when you're away.
Vinay Age 12

A mom is someone who always asks you to do something when you're just about to do something else.
Genevieve

Moms have to do all the washing because dads throw their smelly socks around.
Jacqueline Age 10

A mother is a person who gets married to a man and then she has babies. The baby calls her mother. The baby does the same. She marries when she is older and then she has babies like her mother.
Clara Ortega Age 8

A mother is a lady who finds a man and they reproduce.
Samantha Age 9

Moms wash and dry football uniforms, five minutes before going to school, having only been given them that morning.
Michael Haworth-Maden Age 12

A mom is not really a mom if she does not go to bingo two or three times a week.
Andrew Age 13

A mom is someone who always stands up for you when your dad gets cross with you.
Melissa

A mother is a lady that is afraid of mice and lizards and frogs and toads and crayfish and salamanders and alligators and all of those reptiles — and loves funny bunnies and ducks too — and only the best is me.
Peter Todd Carlson Age 7

A mom is someone who sings in the kitchen.
Elisabeth Fenton Age 12

Mothers are like volcanoes
About muddy puddles on the floor.
Like prehistoric monsters
Like cars screaching
On a wet morning.
Mothers are kind-hearted
Mothers have to be in a hurry
When the door bell goes
The telephone rings
The baby cries
They all start at once.
Some mothers get in a rage
Rushing all over the place
My mother does.   *Philip Age 7*

God created mother because he could not be present everywhere.

Taniya Sharma Age 15

Mammy

*Dale Mayers
Age 6*

Multi-purpose mamas

When you split your pants she does the stitches.
When you eat a frog she whips your britches

When your sick in bed and dont feel good
She always runs and gets your food.

Most people take their moms for granted
If a kid believes this his head is slanted.

When your down and out and have no friends
The love from your mother never ends.

To me in the world there is no other.
Than to have and love your very own mother.

Chris Age 13

A mother is a helper
A finder of lost things
A pocket money giver
An angel without wings.

Laura Dalgleish Age 8

My mom is a Jack of all trades and a master of none.
She is a nurse when we are ill, a gardener, a chef, cooks
super meals, a waitress, a decorator, a cleaning lady, a
dressmaker when she makes or knits our clothes, a fruit-
picker, a book-keeper when she keeps a budget on her
housekeeping, a cleaner, an ironer and most of all she is
an Indian (when she's on the warpath).   *Julie Age 13*

A mom is a person who will coach the football game
when the coach is sick and who will love me to the end of
time.   *Amy Mudya Age 9*

9

Motherhood

In the Ancient Greek language "mitera" means one who gives life. A mother is the beginning of life. All my family naturally go to my mother when we have any troubles because she is the "heart" of our home.

Mirto Azina Age 14

A mother is love.
Candy Manley Age 8

Moms are people who try to make your world beautiful.
Jackie Morgan Age 13

Imagine a tower of bricks, the key brick is the very bottom one, for if we take this one out, they all fall down. Our tower is comprised of our ambitions, our hobbies, our hopes and our dreams, with our mother at the bottom. If we take her away, everything crashes down to become broken dreams and fears. Mothers are our making, and if we have a nasty, sarcastic mother we, too, will be like that. If we have a pleasant, happy, generous mother, that is how we turn out.
Sara Robinson

In my opinion a mother loves her children unconditionally.

Paola Benvisto Age 12

Margaret Danou (opposite) Age 8   *Lisa Vassiliades Age 8*

Life without them

To all moms everywhere, what would we do without you? Who would do our cleaning and cooking? I certainly wouldn't do it all. What! Wash smelly socks and grubby shirts. Burn my hands in hot, fatty, soapy water, no fear! I'd rather not be born.
Lisa Ollard Age 13

If I had not got a mother my bed would not be done and I would be staying up late watching television. I would all ways be spending my money on things that I would not need. At school I would be a little Dracula and so no one would like me. So I am glad to have a mom.
Michael Jenkins Age 10

Without a mother the world would go koo-koo. And I would get sick and I would have no one to love. Then I would die. So I'm glad I got a mother, are you?
Kathleen Singel Age 10

Without a mother the household would always be squabbling and there would never be roasts on Sunday.
Jane Moppel Age 12

If it was not for Mom we would look like a sack of potatoes.

Tony Martin Age 12

Karen Barnett Age 9

What would it be like without a mother?
Have you ever thought?
What would it be like to be an orphan?
How would you like to be bought?

So love you mother all you can,
While you have her now.
She won't be there all your life,
So love her all you can, with all you know how.

Sheryl A. Hartley Age 12

13

Bonnie Thedell

Mothers do not die because they live in the hearts of their children.

Berna Tahmiscioglu Age 16

In tribute

My mother means morning. A beautiful morning.

Abby Age 7

A mom is when deep down inside there is love.

Aldo A. Gomez Age 7

Mothers are the most beautiful thing that has happened to you and they will always be thair, even when your troubled or just want love. *John Age 13*

It is lovely to have a mom. Moms are lovely people and I am going to be a lovely mom when I grow up.

Estelle Moreton

A mom is sombody who always understands your feelings, special feelings, that only my mother and I will ever know about. A person you'll always remember, the rest of your life. My mom. *Karen Angelini Age 10*

My mother helps me with my homework and keeps our home warm with love. *Toby Gutierrez Age 11*

A mom is a person who cares for you and tucks you in at night. When you've made a mistake she says it's quite allright. Someday you will have to grow out of this stage.

Mom doesn't want to let you out of her big lovable cage. When it's time to leave her and face the big wide world, Always remember: She is the one who cares and she will always shed the most tears. *Jan Menno Age 13*

15

Funny Mom

They're really very delightful things, always the best in the world, although quite often very silly things.

Stephen

Mommy does not like maniacs who drive on the road. She also does not like alligators or spiders in her bed.

Sean McDonald Age 7

My mom is going to have a baby and she told me that she can't smack me till after April. *Simon Age 10*

My mom says "Yes dear" when she does not know what I am talking about. *Tanya Age 10*

The way mom worries about my school tests, you would think she was taking them not me.

Robert Booth Age 12

When my mommy talks on the telephone she talks fancy. *Hilary Age 7*

My mom likes watching old fogies' programs on television, but she's kind — and that is all that matters.

Rachel Age 11

My mommy calls me her little tweedy-twer-heart and my sister her goosy. *Clare Aldridge*

A mom doesn't like traveling at 90 mph

Graeme Riddell

Mom's like a football. She gets knocked around a bit, but always stays the same shape. *Mark Age 11*

Truely most of the time Mom is a lovable thing, although she has got a knack for breaking plates, cups etc. quite a lot. And it's only very rarely that she trips up when she's carrying the rubbish out. *Jane Age 13*

My mommy gets me round the bend because she once put butter in the washing machine. *Tracey Age 8*

If she ran for President she would convince everyone that she's the best one. The way she can talk. *Leroy Vancourt Age 10*

The trouble with moms is that they don't play games though she gives me a few rotten under arm pitches in the summer. *John Age 10*

A mother is for wakeing you up, telling you your shirt is on backward when your half asleep, kissing you off to school then remembering its Saturday! *Gretchen Ackerman Age 11*

Moms are funny things!

Moms are sometimes fussy
About manners and being good;
They're always telling boys and girls
About the things they should

Remember when they're out at friends,
Like manners — "Do say 'please'
And thank the lady nicely when you
know it's time to leave."

At bath-time there are orders
Like "Don't forget your feet,
Remember dry yourself quite well
And leave the bathroom neat."

But if ever I was judging,
Then with banners all unfurled,
I'd place a crown upon her head
And vote my mom — "Miss World."

John Elliott

Adele Cox Age 9

Useful people to have around

A mother usually insists that you learn (or try to) a musical instrument.

You are taken to an aged piano teacher, and learn that a rest is a musical term as well as a nap.

You learn other things from them too. Nobody lives on Mars, Mass = Density + volume (or the other way around?) and not to put your knife in your mouth. In other words, you start to accumalate a small store of knowledge.

They are useful people to have around.

David Honigmann Age 9

Putting up with us kids

God didn't have enough arms for keeping kids out of trouble so he invented moms. *Alice Lumpkin Age 11*

If I were my mother, sometimes I would smack me hard. *Diena Lees Age 11*

My mom has weird rules that I have to obey, like having a bath, keeping my bedroom neat and even having my hair cut. *Christopher Moates Age 12*

Mom says I'm nicest when I am asleep because I can not say anything wrong. *Richard Age 12*

Philippa Age 8

If I were my mother my children would go to bed at 10 o'clock at night and get up at ten in the morning too. They would not have to take vitamin pills or drink milk of magnesia if they had tummy aches. They would have a dollar a week allowance. The children would be sent to school once a week just to keep up the good education. When it was a birthday I would not insist on inviting someone like Cecilia Pigface to the party.   *Katy Berger Age 11*

Moms are people who don't believe you when you fake sick.   *Jo Ellyn Shindel Age 10*

The best think I thought Mom did was having me, but others might not think so.   *Tim Tripp Age 12*

David Age 7

21

Isn't she a pain

Moms are the sort of people who, before a movie starts in the evening, send you to bed saying how awful it will be and then wake you up saying what a fantastic movie it was.

Nicholas

I don't like the way my mom puts me to bed. When I am wide awake at night, she makes me go to sleep, and when I'm fast asleep in the morning, she makes me get up!

Stephen

The one problem with my mom is she is allways cleaning up, if you put anything down and go away for a minuet when you come back to it, it has been put away.

Ian

John Age 9

Pinickity, pinackity
Lilickety, lilackity
Just like a mother hen
Or even like a mother wren.

It's "Clean your room!"
Or "Don't touch the broom"
"Don't eat too fast.
Make your food last."

P. Tucker

Mommy cleans up our rooms and throws my teddy bear's head away.

Steven

Mothers are funny things really because you never know whether there going to shout at you or not. They say do your bedroom and while your doing your bedroom they tell you to do the stairs and before you know it you have a hole load of jobs to do before your even finished your bedroom. I sometimes wonder where they get them all from.

Heather Age 10

A mom is a person who you can't tell what to do because mother knows best.

Elaine Age 14

I have never been allowed to stay up and see a Dracula movie yet. My mom says I need sleep so I can work hard at school next day, but I think she sends me to bed so she can watch television in peace.

Billie Mayhook Age 13

A mom is a person who worries about you, and won't come to a touchfootball game cause she thinks I'll get hurt. A mom is a person that WORRIES!!

Scott E. Waise Age 10

Sean Charlton
Age 8

Twenty-one today

When I ask Mom how old she is she always says twenty-one. As I have a sister who is twenty-two even dumb old me knows this cannot be right.

Billie Mayhook Age 13

I think my mom is good looking and so do very many other people. She has dark brown hair and dark brown eyes. You have to give her credit. She is forty-one.

Debbie Age 13

My mother is a teacher and she knows the answers to most questions except what age she is.

Douglas A. Currie Age 13

My mom has been thirty-four for the last three years.

Louise

Nicola Breakwell
Age 7

Marrina Age 9

Gab, gab

The habit no mom should be without is gabbing on the phone; no mom would be complete without it.

Miles Hutchinson Age 10

My mom is quiet but can be gabby at times and one thing she can't stand is been stood out on the street gabbing away, she would much rather sit down and gab over a cup of coffee.

Dave Age 14

She is always going on about her and her sister when she was small, I pretend to listen but I watch TV instead. We just say YEH, YEH, YEH. She soon shuts up.

Timothy

My mom is always talking and the only time she is quiet is when she is very interested in what's on television and even then she puts in a quick comment. She is also quiet when she is asleep.

Julie Age 9

James Age 8

27

Going out

I think my mom is funny because when she plans to go out she has to do her hair, her face and by the time she has finished, it is to late to go out. *Ean Age 10*

Every time Mommy goes out to a dance she puts her false nails on, and she looks ever so funny, and Daddy puts aftershave on, and he smells as well. *Elisabeth Age 7*

My mother powders her face,
Puts lipstick on,
And cover herself in perfume,
That's why my father disowns her at parties. *Sophia Age 11*

Samantha Goulding
Age 8

Andrea Scown
Age 7

Moms make you go to the barbers as though you were a poodle being got ready for a dog show.

Peter Wilkinson Age 11

Volker Age 14

Learn . . . or else!

Mommys are nice except when they find gum sticking to their carpet.

Michelle Jones Age 10

Moms are vultures that hang over you, telling you that you have to take out the garbage again. They nag at you, giving you lectures on life in general and how to make your bed in particular.

Peter

Moms should not be allowed to start nagging and the best way to stop her is to keep neat.

Philippa

My mom smacks me when I am naughty it hurts me very much but I deserve it.

Stephen Age 9

What ever my mom does wrong
I still love her.

Barry Silverman Age 10

Wendy Age 6

Do you know I was born because I wanted to be near my mommy? *Claudia Martinez Age 8*

32

Mom and me

My mom is kind and gentle. Sometimes my mother really loves me and she looks at my face and she smiles at me. I go and sit by her.

Balbinder Kaur Kalsi Age 11

My mommy always makes me happy when I'm sad, when I fall she put plaster on my leg when I get a cut on my leg she cuddles me. She still loves me although I'm very naughty sometimes. When I'm grown up I'm going to be a nice mommy and happy like my mommy.

Leela Salmon Age 9

My Mommy some times calls me Funny names and When I do naughty things and I tell the truth she kisses me.

Mark Grundy Age 6

Alison Baker Age 7

33

In Mommy's arms

My mother always has room for me in her arms. She's never too busy to give our family the special love a mother can only give. *Donna Jauga Age 9*

My mother cares for me. I feel that I've got day and night protection when I'm near her. *Martha van Kees Age 9*

Mom is a person you can come to for comfort, when all hope is lost, like an old teddy bear with one eye and half an ear. *Patricia Bowie Age 13*

Moms are always busy but never too busy to give you a quick cuddle. *Helen Rankin Age 9*

My mom is nice to sit on. She's nice and soft and bouncey. *Paul Fanneaux Age 10*

Hadas Nahari Age 9

My mother's hands

These hands lifted me when I was a baby. They dried away the tears when I cried at night or when I was upset. My first food came from her hands. She helped me tie my laces, hold the spoon in my hands, shampooed and bathed me. I remember the sadness I felt when I let go of her hands on my first day at school. Although they may get old and wrinkled I will always remember what those precious hands did for me.

Sean McGilligam

My mother's hands can be soft and hard. They are like smooth silk when she is rubbing my cheeks, and like hot fire when my mother is smacking me for being naughty. They do loving things like combing my hair, cleaning my ears and taking care of my clothes. They do sweet things like making cookies, cakes and candy. If I had to give my mother's hands a grade they would get a B+. If it wasn't for the spankings her hands would get a big "A."

Kim Wilkinson

She brushes my hair so it is not tangly.

Jeri Cothran 8

The comforter

She rubs your tummy and gives you warm milk when you feel you're really in a big round ball.   *Millicent Greer*

When ever I hurt myself my mom will go and rescue me, as though I had broken my back when I barely grazed my knee.   *Alison Hancock Age 11*

Moms are for sitting by your side whenever you need her.   *Randy Taylor Age 11*

My mom cares. She worries about me. I feel like I am always next to her. She makes me feel loved when she stands by my side.   *Stephen McDonough Age 10*

A mother is someone who comforts you. Because she misses you, even for one minute. Because you are her child.   *Kristin Thompson Age 8*

Bjarne Kalo Age 11

Cooked with love

When I come home from school, who would be there to make a delicious hot chocolate and maybe some hot cookies or a quick snack of goodies before having a proper dinner. I might have spaghetti bolognaise with a rich luscious pudding, oozing with cream and "jimmies" sprinkled carefully over the top. Or another night I might have spam and potato with salt and pepper laid over them, not forgetting to dribble the tomato sauce over everything. Only a nice, welcoming mom could do that, making things just exactly how you like them.

Lisa Cllard Age 13

A mother is a person that when she bakes a cake she lets you lick the bowl. *Dominique Black Age 10*

A mom is someone who cares about you. So she cooks for you. *Lisa Heder Age 7½*

Even when you don't like what your mother's cooking, remember, she puts her hands, heart and love into it. *Debbie Day Age 10*

A mother is a person who always has hot cocoa ready for you when you come inside from playing out in the snow, and lemonade for when you come inside from playing in the hot summer sun. *Debbie Wernstein Age 10*

A mom is somebody who always keeps the cooky jar full! *Chris Kline Age 9*

Diets

Daddy each day says, "Darling, why don't you eat something. You will be very ill." Mom gets up every morning at 6 o'clock and eats her diet biscuit, which she says contains a whole breakfast of bacon and eggs. Then poor Mom because she has woken up *so* early, by midday, she gets in a temper! So we all go to a Kentucky Fried Chicken Place, because she is too tired to cook. Well I don't know, I do hope she stops soon. *Wendy Age 13*

My mom is on a diet, a *eating* DIET! *Paul Age 9*

Mom doesn't have any will-power diet because she isn't very fat and she doesn't have any will-power.
Naral Age 12

Some nights my mom says that she is going to diet. So she cuts down on potatoes, and sugar in her coffee. Then we are sitting watching the television she gets through a pound of candy! (Or my dad buys some cakes) Then my mom says "I think I'll start my diet tomorrow." I don't think my mom has ever been on a strict diet in her life but then she would not be the same cuddly Mom if she was slim. *Jane Age 12*

A mother is quite kind because if she's having a sneaky eat she gives you something too. *Mark Dowling Age 12*

Mom —
Likes antiques
Has even restored some
But hasn't succeeded
With her figure.
Matthew Age 11

Belgin Akyol Age 13

39

Like a rose

My mother is medium sized, brown in color and as cool as a cucumber. Her hair is red and thick. She has a proud walk, and is as tender as a chicken. A rose is as beautiful as my mother, and she is as fresh as a daisy, and as strong as an ox.

When I grow up I would like to be as beautiful as my mother. And have the beautiful ways she has. My mother is more precious than gold.   *Carmen Ramnath Age 11*

My mom is the coolest person in the world. Sometimes she looks like a rose and other times she is just a plain daisy. When she is a rose you can imagine that my mom is very nice.   *Wanda Michels Age 11*

Mandy Clee Age 10

Abbas Age 8

41

Mom is always there

Always a friendly smile,
Always open arms
Willing to help while —
Troubles are at their worst.
The door is always open
To us their children.

Elaine Rockley Age 7

Alexandra Hitchings

It's Mom!

When things go wrong
And everything you do goes dong!
Who's always there with smile and help
Comfort, love, or if you need it a scalp?
It's MOM.

We mutter and we mumble and chaff
Because Mom says, "No it isn't safe!"
But who knows when to pull the rein
Or give the children their way again?
It's MOM.

And when you come home moping, sad
Or maybe just plain hopping mad
Who knows what's best
To sooth the raging in your breast?
It's MOM.   *Ian Laurenson Age 11*

When all other friends have deserted you, Mom is
always here.   *Catherine Woodall Age 14*

Moms versus dads

A mom is a female parent. Sometimes you don't want to eat what she tells you, and then you end up not eating supper. But, sometimes, she tells your dad, and then you end up eating your supper.
Kim McCabe Age 10

Moms are people who will not tell Dad if you didn't clean your room.
Brad Osborne Age 10

You must obey your mother or she'll get father.
Joann Jenkins Age 11

Moms are people who end up doing chores your father told you to do.
Gary Crees Age 13

Moms are people who tell you to "go ask your father."
Elaine Hartman Age 14

A mother is the one who convinces Dad to let the children do something that he absolutely forbade when he was first asked.
Laurie Lujan Age 11

A mother is the parent that cooks your food, washes your clothes, and tells your father when to spank you.
Keith Bridges Age 12

If I am naughty I always break it to my mom first.
David Age 12

Take care of your mom

If you have a mother, give her all your loving care, for you won't know her value, until you see her empty chair.
Mona Fouad El Sakka Age 16

Moms deserve a couple of surprises and treats themselves, for all the hard work they do.
Louise Twaite

With all her worrying about her children, Mother seldom has time to worry about herself. There are, of course, advertisements and posters telling parents to take care of their children such as:
"A lesson in life" and
"Under your feet is better than under a car."
So, why not have posters saying:
"Take care of your Mom, she's valuable."
Alison Bain

A mother is a person to hold tight, and care for.
Alpoistan Gumunain   *Sarah McKenzie Age 11*

Berrin
Suboiy

45

She's an old softie

A mom is probably the most likley one to give in
to you.
Jessica Age 11

I like my mom best because I don't get smacked
so much.
Paul Age 8

A mom is a person who cries when you do something
bad, and cries even harder when you do something good.
Robin DiBiase Age 14

Although she seems strict enough
Underneath the skin that's all Bluff.
Samantha Worseldine Age 10

Even the roughest of mothers are very gentle and
kind inside, or else they could not be mothers.   *Elaine Wong*

Whenever she gets upset she expresses her feelings
angrily, but afterward she is sorry about the harsh things
she said and gives us cookies to show us she loves us.
Avery Age 15

My mom is a bit stupid because every time I ask for
something she buy's it me.
Debbie Age 10

I have a super mother who makes cakes, puts them in
the pantry and doesn't notice when I eat them.
Mark Wickham-Jones Age 13

A mother never likes to scold her children even
though she knows she has to.   *Julia Macdonald-Smith Age 13*

Marilyn Norman Age 8

Kenneth

My mom isn't really a beauty queen, but in my heart she is the prettiest woman in the world.

Ian Age 10

Beautiful in her own way

My mom is as beautiful as anyone can be, well maybe not to everyone but always to me. Now I don't mean always by looks because you learn all that junk from TV and books. But I mean that she has a beauty inside.

Donna Nitte Age 12

My mother is very kind and when she was younger she was very very pretty. Now she is a bit plump but I like her very very much, she seems to be prettier each day. She doesn't know how to cook very well but when she cooks the dinner it seems to have something special about it. When she makes my bed I think she puts something into it, and I don't awake all night.

Conchita Rey Benayas Age 10

My mom's, well, she's beautiful in her own way. She's not exactly Miss World 1977, but you can't just go and draw a picture of her and say "That's mom." There's something about her, whether it's her willingness to listen or what. I don't know.

Daryl Mitchell

A slave to her family

My mom has not got any hobbies I suppose her hobbey is cleaning the house.

Craig Age 9

A mother is the parent that plays house all the time.

Keith Bridgee Age 12

Mothers have to wash your hair when they don't want to, and buy you clothes when they don't have any money.

Aaron Sumler

Most people think of her as just a cleaner. A mother is someone special.

Bobby Age 10

"What's for supper Mom!"

I see my mom a standing against the kitchen sink,
Scrubbing dishes one by one with wrinkled hands all
   covered with soap.
Michael yelling all the time makes Mom go round the
   bend.
Making breckfast, lunches, dinners.
Mom, when work is nearly done
Hears the fearful cry again
"What's for supper Mom!!!"

Julie

I sometimes think that they are bossy and bad-tempered but when I think about it I realize how hard it is to be a mom. It is make breakfast, wash up, go shopping, cook dinner, wash up, put feet up, collect the kids from school. I can see why they ask you to wash up or get your own cookie. I begin to wonder why they ever become mothers in the first place.   *Alan Age 15*

Who would want to be a mother?

Everyday you clean the house listening to soap operas on the radio while you sweep, dust and polish, making our beds, scorching your hands washing dishes, or trying to make the old washing machine work. When all the cleaning's done you can have a rest with a snack and last month's paper which you still have not read. Then there is the shopping and hurry to meet the schoolbus. Homework comes next. "Mommy how do you do this" or "Mommy how do you do that." After supper, Mom's favorite program comes on, but of course you have to wash the dishes, darn Dad's socks, or sew buttons on school shirts. When she has finished all she is fit for is bed.

Perhaps I do not really want to be a mother after all.

Susan Godfrey

Nicolas Bork Mann
Age 14

Poor working Moms

My mother is very patient. She would have to be with five kids, four dogs and two jobs. *Pam Repec Age 12*

My mother gets up between six and halfpast a.m. and she does some general housework and makes breakfast. At seven she wakes up my two brothers and they all have breakfast. Then Mommy gets the boys ready for school, wakes up Daddy, and at quarter to eight she goes off to work. *Joanna Blake Age 11*

I wish my mother din't go to work becase I love her. *Danielle Age 8*

My Mom Christmas Shopping

Maxine Howitt Age 10

52

A mom is a superwoman who can be in two places at once. She can tie two pairs of sneakers with one hand and stir the pudding with the other. That's what a mom is.

Judy McDonough Age 10

She does a hell of a job feeding and clothing us!

Paul Age 13

My mom is the best. She can work, clean, cook and wash and take care of six kids too. *Kellie Harlam Age 10*

A mom is someone who is responsible for cooking or cleaning. Not all mom's do that because a dad can do it too. *Chris Age 12*

A mother's place is in the home, but my mom doesn't think so. *Darren Age 11*

A mother is not just a mother, she is a Human Being too.
Barbara Allbritton Age 11

My mom she works so very hard.
She must be near to tears,
Cos' gimie, gimie! More, More!
Are the only words she hears.

She only wants the magic word,
Oh by the way it's PLEASE
She acts just like a servant,
But never asks for fees.
Susan Harvie Age 10

Petra Hammond Age 9

Temper, temper

On a whole we all love her, except those times when she wallops us.
Robin Age 12

She gets mad when all of us done something bad on the same day, and that's the time when you shouldn't bother her too much.
Juanita

When my mom's angry she is like a two ton truck going down hill.
Martin Age 10

She Sometimes gets mad and once She got So mad that She made us make our own Breakfast.
Mark Age 9

Sometimes mom's can be dangerous like dragging you out of the room by your hair, or the famous clip around the ear.
Paul Age 9

My mom is very kind and helpful, but she has her bad times bang crash wallop ouch!

John Age 9

Our mom doesn't often spank us but when she does, she does.

Surjit Age 11

Mom gets up at 7:30 am and begins her routine day of housework, headaches, and yelling.

Mark Age 13

I think your mother still loves you even when she shouts and raves at you.

Amanda Age 10

Thank you

My mother is so kind I do not no how to thank Mom. How can I thank you my Mom?

David Webb Age 9

Mother, at every difficult moment in my life I turn to you. You are the only person who can help me whenever I need help, the only person who can make a sacrifice for me. That will be understood only by children who have lost their mothers.

Savva Evangelia Age 17

Who do you go to when
You're in a mess?
Who do you turn to when
You're in distress?

Who gives you money
When you are flat broke?
Who explains why you're late
When you're out with a bloke?

Of course its your mother
Who else could it be?
Give her a treat sometimes
Perhaps make coffee.

*Caroline
de Silva
Age 9*

Remember her birthday
And Mother's Day too
You look after her
And she'll look after you!

Debbie Russell Age 16

Be nice to your mother. Don't let her be your work horse, will you?

Donald Ryan Age 8

To a very special "Mother"

This verse is just meant to be, a very special way of saying, "Thank you, Mother."

It isn't easy to express the things I want to say,
For what goes on unnoticed, every single day.
So Mom, and all others, a tribute to you,
For you are truly the "Queens" of the world.
(P.S. Don't be a bit worried, Dad, because you aren't so bad.)

Jesse O'Neill Age 13

To Mama,   I hope   you   bring us
up propaly   from Dominic

Iris Harcel

A tribute to my mom

There are four children including me, all girls, and although my mom does two part time cleaning jobs, and runs the home, she always has time to help us, to teach us things, to make us things and to cuddle us all every day.

We are all very close to our mom I think we are unusually close, because I see my mom do things for us that I think other moms wouldn't bother to do. Mom goes around at night to us and we have a little chat about things. Although my mom believes in strictness we can always talk to our mom about any problems we have.

When I grow up, I will always remember my childhood with great happiness. I never ever want to leave mom. She said we will grow up and have our own children one day. I can only hope I can be as unselfish with my own children as my mom is.   *Donna Banyard Age 11*

Mother: trusting, loveing, nise, helpfull. Sombody care for you. Sombody nise.   *Craig Age 7*

A mother is a person at has babies becaues her is kind.

Gabrielle Age 9

Lessons in life

A good mother is worth a hundred teachers. The teacher teaches lessons from books while the good mother teaches everything that is useful in life.

Mona Fouad El Sakka Age 16

When I cried, I remember my mother used to tell me how to overcome sadness. She explained to me that the world is full of evil, and if I didn't learn to be strong I would fail. And when she knew I was strong enough to face reality she began to teach me how to find my way in life. She told me that I must learn to be kind, to be a good friend, and always to be ready to help. But I think the most important thing I learned was to trust myself. It gave me a lot of confidence. My parents gave me the basic values I needed, and because they taught me how to learn, I learned all the other things by myself. And for that I thank and love them.

Michal Arlosoroff Age 17

And as I grew
She shared good times with me,
She taught me to be realistic and understanding,
She taught me how a mother should be
But most importantly, she taught me
How to be a woman.

Debra Duel Age 15

Jessica Gould

59

A mother is . . .

A mother is the one who, after only nine months of introduction, loves you for the rest of your life.

Kevin Sheridan

A mother is a loving angel. Between her arms you find warmth and love which you can never find anywhere else.

Shahira Yossef Age 16

A mother is a person that cares for you, getting out of her hot cozy bed in the middle of the night, giving you milk, when she could have slept on, and not bothered.

Brid Ni Chonghoile Age 14

A mother is a person who loves her children even when she smacks us.

Roger Age 8

Jesper Tønnesen Age 8

Sarah Cakebread Age 10

Kim Bernabe Age 7

Eugenia Escribano

Tony Lynn Age 10

Rupa Age 8

Andrew Green

Lars Age 8

61

Mother is kind today.
Mother was kind yesterday.
Mother is kind every day.
Mother makes kindness.
Daniel Bajnath Age 10

A watchful eye, a gentle touch,
That happy laugh we love so much,
In every home, there is no other,
Who loves and cares just like a mother.
Gabrielle Smylie Age 12

*Claire
Jones
Age 6*

A mom is someone who is lovely and cudly.
Chris Dry Age 9

A mom is someone to lean on when you're falling.
Jackie Morgan Age 13

A mother is someone who tresures gifts that you gave
to her.
Robert Redding Age 8

Moms are really groovey. Helping us when we
are sick. Washing, drying, all the lot. Moms are hard
working ladies busy here, busy there, busy nearly
everywhere.
Ruth Shaw

Mother . . . That was the first word that I learned
when I was little. And she was the first person I knew
and loved.
Berna Tahmiscioglu Age 16

A mother's worry never ends for her children.
Sheryl A. Hartley Age 12

A mother's smile can give you a little happyness
when your sad.
Amanda Davey Age 10

Mother is a special gift, that God has given to me.
Rookminee Chatergoon Age 11

"Mom" is the only word that makes everybody all
over the world happy.
Hasan Ali Tolgay Age 17

Moms have a heart with a key; they open it and love pours out.

Marcia Age 9

Claire Mullan Age 9

Mothers are people that tell the boys to let her little sweet girl play football.
Mary Lyle Scott Age 10

A mom is someone that teaches you how to play baseball even though she is a lady and wears high heel shoes!
Debra Trujillo Age 11

A mom is someone who has to wash faces and count heads when she's ready to go somewhere.
Melonie Dixon Age 11

A mom is someone who always knows when there is something wrong even if you don't tell her. *Lisa Tresa Age 14*

A mom is a large girl that buys food for you and your family.
Mike Bell Age 8¾

A mom is someone to help you eat your food when you can't eat it all, so it looks like you ate it all.
Teri Burns Age 11

Moms are people who sit up worrying about you and when you come home they holler at you. *Gary Crees Age 13*

Some mothers' apron strings are never cut, just streched.
Patricia Sisti Age 14

When Dad drives we get yelled at. But! When Mom drives we get whistled at.
Roger Krause Age 8